This Walker book belongs to:

_____

_____

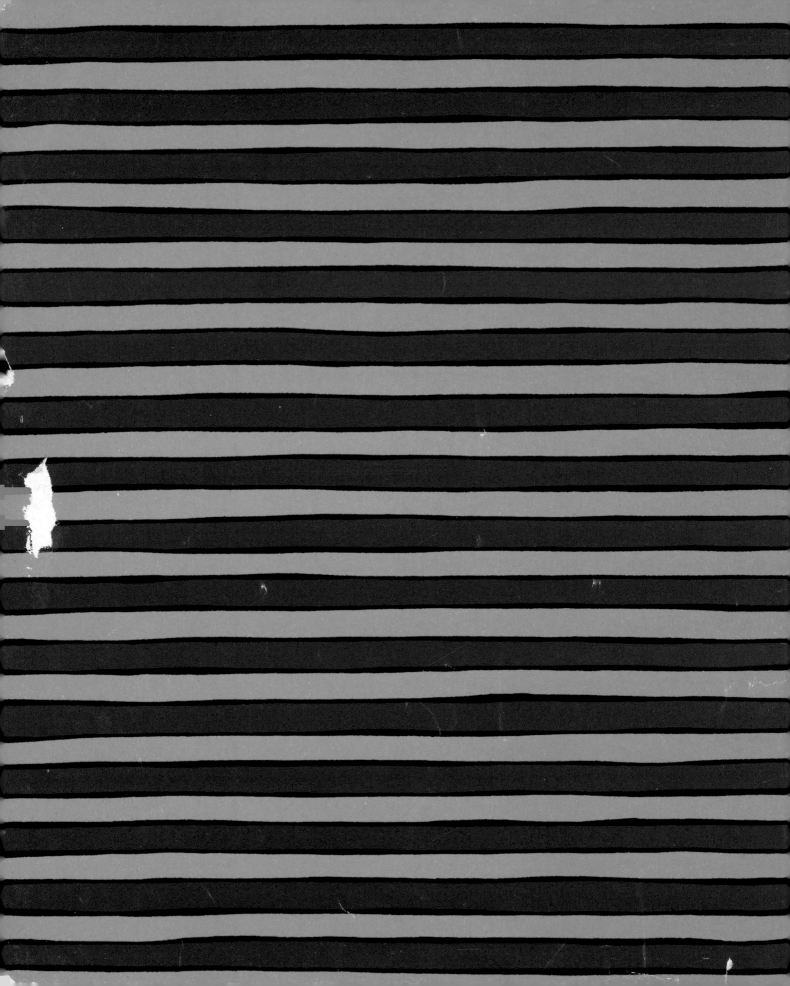

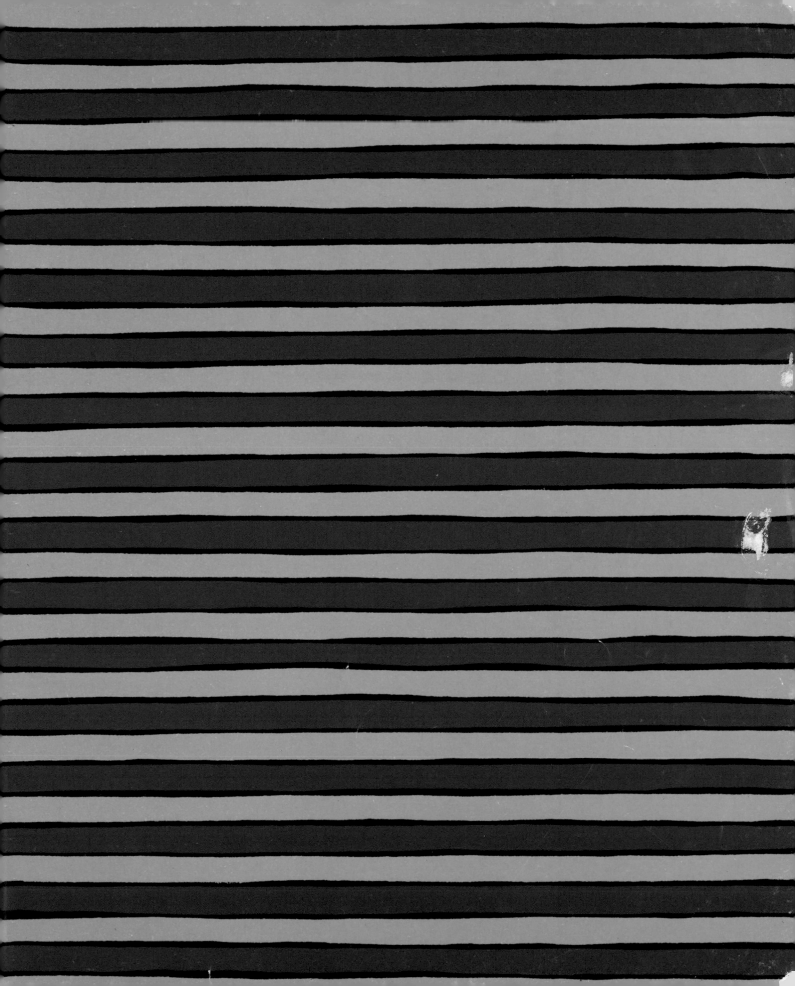

Text first published 1985
by HarperCollins Publishers Ltd
First published in 1994
by Walker Books Ltd
87 Vauxhall Walk
London SE11 5HJ

This edition first published 2008

2 4 6 8 10 9 7 5 3 1

Text © 1985 Judy Hindley
Illustrations © 1994 Nick Sharratt

The moral rights of the author
and illustrator have been asserted.

This book has been typeset in Garamond Book Educational.

Printed in China

British Library Cataloguing in Publication Data:
a catalogue record for this book is available.
from the British Library

ISBN 978-1-4063-1669-8

www.walkerbooks.co.uk

Crazy ABC

Judy Hindley

Illustrated by
Nick Sharratt

WALKER BOOKS
AND SUBSIDIARIES

LONDON • BOSTON • SYDNEY • AUCKLAND

Aa

Axe in the apple tree –

what else begins like that?

Ask an alligator

with an apple

on his hat.

Ff

Fie! Fo!

There's a fly on my nose!

What other funny things

can you see?

A frog on my foot,

a flea on my knee!

Gg

Gooey goose gravy – isn't it good?

Glassful of grape-juice, glug, glug, glug.

Hh

Ho, ho, ho!

How shall I be happy?

I'll hop until I'm happy,

I'll hide until you find me,

and then I'll have a hug.

Ho, ho, ho!

Ii

"Ick!" said the Indian.

"It
is
ITCHY
in
this
outfit!"

Jj

What do you like

that starts with *j*?

Do you like jelly?

Do you like jam?

Do you like to jump

as high as you can?

Kk

Here is a kite

fit for a king!

Here is a king

in the kite string.

Give it a kick!

Ll

Look, look,

look what I can do!

Leap high…

Lie low…

Lick a lovely lolly.

Mm

The mountaineer

has lost his map.

What a mess!

What a muddle!

Oh, where is his mum?

Nn

No, no, no!

This isn't nice!

Here is a ninny

with a nut on his nose,

and a noodle on his necktie!

No, no, no!

Oo

Odd! It's an omelette!

An omelette falling off!

And here we see an officer

with omelette on top.

Pp

"Pooh!" said the pirate,

peering at his plate of prunes.

What a picky peg-leg,

picking at his *p*s.

Can you find the *p*s?

Pickles, pears, potatoes –

look at all of these!

Qq

Queasy, queasy queen.

She must be feeling sick.

Tuck her in a quilt,

quick, quick, quick!

Rr

Rrrm, rrrm, race-track rider,

racing for a ribbon,

ROARS around the race-track,

rrrm, rrrm, rrrm!

Ss

See here! Sit up straight!

Sip your soup like Mrs Snake.

Sssss – don't slurp!

What a silly sausage!

Tt

Tut, tut, tut,

do you have a *t*?

I have lots of *t*s:

tummy, toes and teeth!

Uu

Up, up, up!

Underneath umbrella.

Upset,

upside down,

making ugly faces.

Vv

Vroom! Vroom!

Very fast van!

Very smashed vegetables,

very sad man.

Ww

Woo, woo, wild wind

whistles round your head.

Wiggly worm,

wicked witch,

warm in bed.

Xx

X-ray.

Exit.

Who's next?

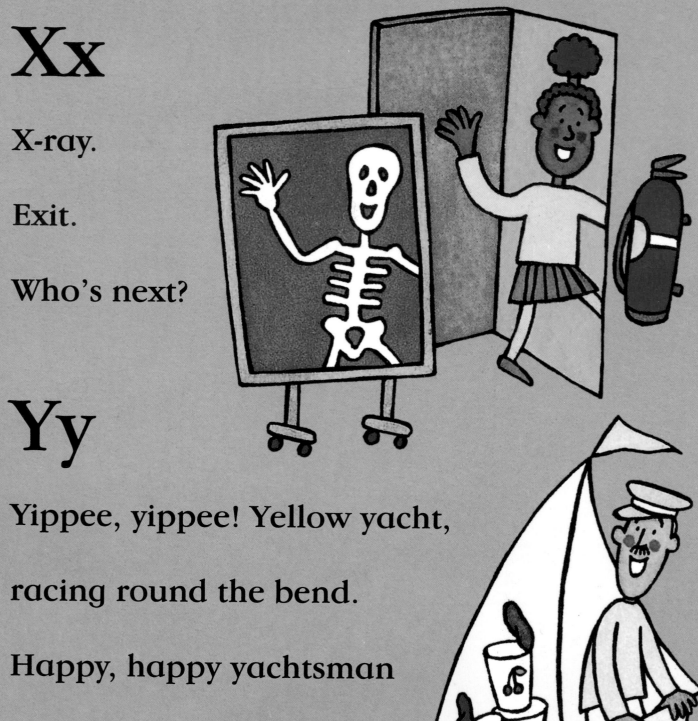

Yy

Yippee, yippee! Yellow yacht,

racing round the bend.

Happy, happy yachtsman

when the day is at an end.

Zz

Zipping in,

zipping up.

ZZZZZZZZzzzzzz

Good night, my friend.

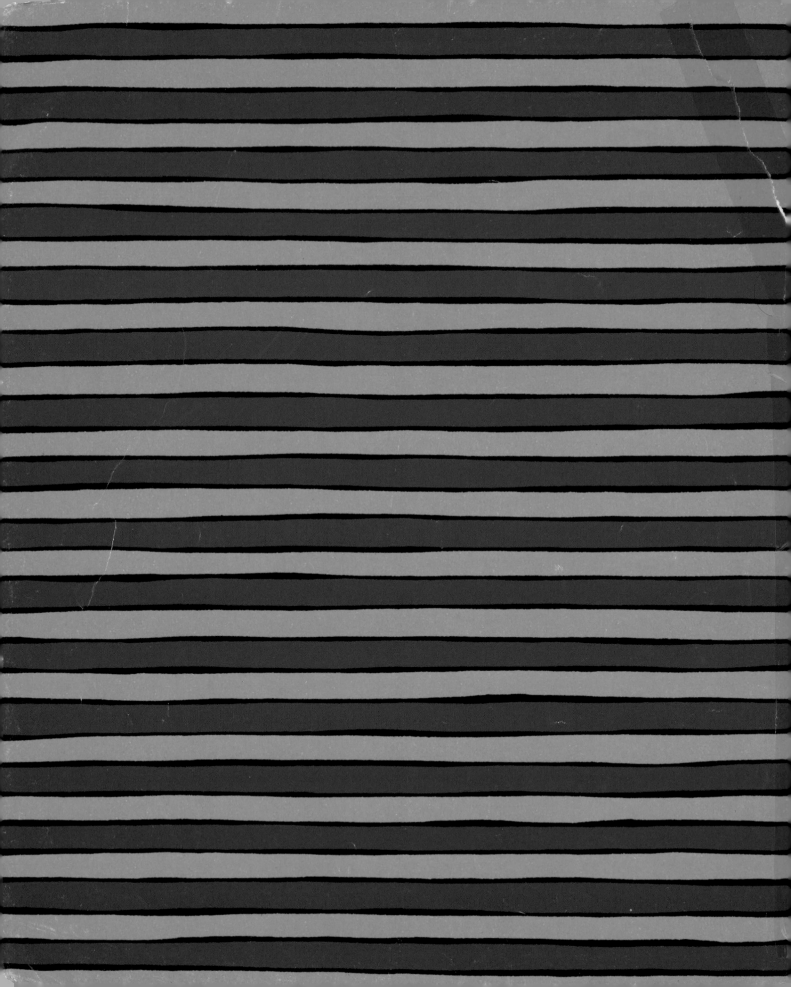

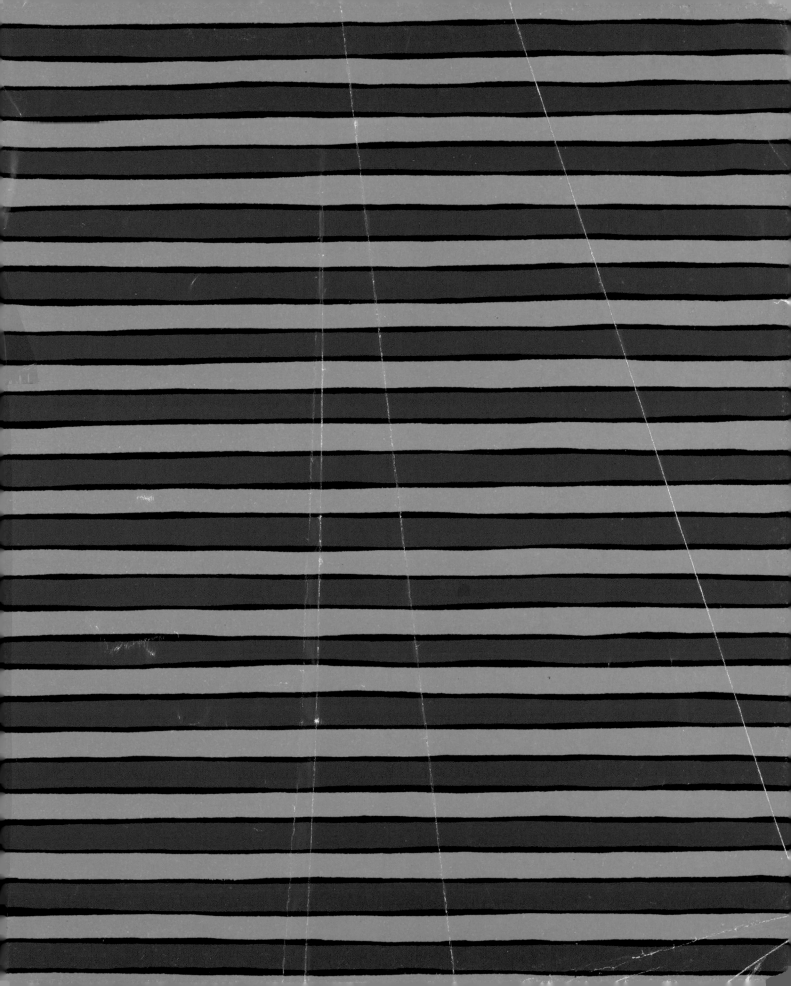

Titles in this series

ISBN 978-1-4063-1669-8

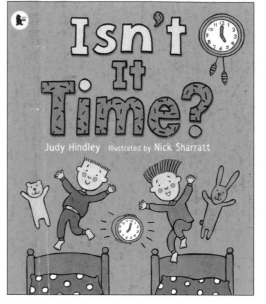

ISBN 978-1-4063-1670-4

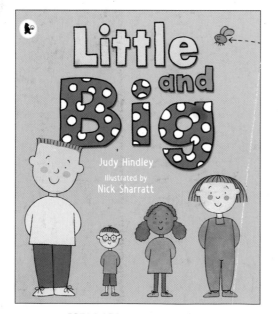

ISBN 978-1-4063-1668-1

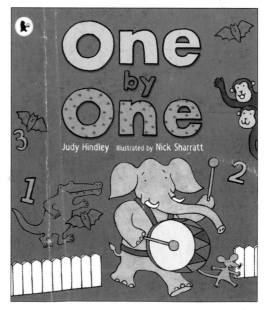

ISBN 978-1-4063-1667-4

Available from all good bookstores

www.walkerbooks.co.uk